MW00897539

LeAnne Blackmore's new book, *God's Name is a Tower*, is a gift to parents and children. In simple poetry and charming images she invites her readers to celebrate the powerful goodness of our God. It is the perfect gift for any child that you want to know about the goodness of God and will be a perfect addition to any family's library. I can hardly imagine the power of making this book a regular part of your bedtime routine. In this book you will find the tool you need to speak truth and beauty and faith into the life of your child.

God's Name is a Tower is rooted in Scripture and declares the goodnesss of God and God's love for us. The beautiful poetry flows directly out of God's Word and makes these timeless truths accessible to children right when they most need to learn of God's love. As I read the book I found myself wishing this beautiful book was in my hands when I was raising my children. What a treasure! Grab a copy today or give one as a gift to a child that you love and you want to know of the confident love of God.

—ETHAN MAGNESS,
Senior Minister at First Christian Church, Johnson City, TN

Children will request *God's Name is a Tower* to be read over and over, being drawn in by the sing-song rhyming pattern. Parents will gladly oblige, knowing that the text is rooted in Scripture and teaches children a lesson about the power of God's love and provision.

—DR. KARIN J. KEITH,
Department Chair, Curriculum and Instruction
East Tennessee State University, Johnson City, TN

As a classical Christian educator I have been trained to understand the developmental characteristics in which learning occurs, and it has been proven over and over again that in the formative years, often referred to as the grammar stage of learning, poetry, chants, songs, and creativity in disseminating information is most effective to capture the mind of the young learner. In short, we must do what we can to make the intent of the written words come alive. In her new book, *God's Name is a Tower*, LeAnne Blackmore is doing just that . . . making the Written Word come alive. What a grand and novel idea to present the character of God in a sing-song format so that these young minds will enjoy the process of learning about the character of God in a way that makes sense to them and in a way that they will be able to easily commit these truths to memory. There's a reason that I can say *hickory, dickory, dock* and each of us can complete the line, and that's because creative, poetic sing-song teaching works, and for that reason I heartily recommend *God's Name is a Tower* for the young, and not so young, learners in your life.

—JERRY WILLIAMS,
School Chancellor for Providence Academy, Johnson City, TN

God's Name is a Tower

LeAnne Blackmore

Ambassador International
GREENVILLE, SOUTH CAROLINA & BELFAST, NORTHERN IRELAND

www.ambassador-international.com

God's Name is a Tower
©2019 by LeAnne Blackmore

All rights reserved

Illustrated by Windha Sukmanindya

ISBN: 978-1-62020-849-6
eISBN: 978-1-62020-881-6

Scripture taken from the NEW AMERICAN STANDARD BIBLE®, Copyright © 1960, 1962, 1963, 1968, 1971, 1972, 1973, 1975, 1977, 1995 by The Lockman Foundation. Used by permission.

Holy Bible, New Living Translation, copyright © 1996, 2004, 2015 by Tyndale House Foundation. Used by permission of Tyndale House Publishers, Inc., Carol Stream, Illinois 60188. All rights reserved.

The ESV® Bible (The Holy Bible, English Standard Version®). ESV® Text Edition: 2016. Copyright © 2001 by Crossway, a publishing ministry of Good News Publishers. The ESV® text has been reproduced in cooperation with and by permission of Good News Publishers. Unauthorized reproduction of this publication is prohibited. All rights reserved.

THE HOLY BIBLE, NEW INTERNATIONAL VERSION®, NIV® Copyright © 1973, 1978, 1984, 2011 by Biblica, Inc.® Used by permission. All rights reserved worldwide.

Page Layout by Hannah Nichols
Ebook Conversion by Anna Riebe Raats

AMBASSADOR INTERNATIONAL
Emerald House
411 University Ridge, Suite B14
Greenville, SC 29601, USA
www.ambassador-international.com

AMBASSADOR BOOKS
The Mount
2 Woodstock Link
Belfast, BT6 8DD, Northern Ireland, UK
www.ambassadormedia.co.uk

The colophon is a trademark of Ambassador, a Christian publishing company.

In loving memory of my Mom & Dad—
who instilled in me
an abiding love and reverence
for our great God.

Psalm 145:4 (NLT) — "Let each generation tell its children of
your mighty acts; let them proclaim your power."

God's name is a tower
To which I can run.
In Him I find safety
Like no other One.

Proverbs 18:10 (ESV) — "The name of the LORD is a strong tower; the righteous man runs into it and is safe."

Psalm 124:8 (ESV) — "Our help is in the name of the LORD . . ."

He is Shepherd
and Judge,
Redeemer and King,
Creator, Provider,
My Everything!

As Shepherd He holds me
And keeps me secure.
His arms are so strong
I'm protected for sure.

Psalm 23:1 (ESV) — "The LORD is my shepherd; I shall not want."

John 3:16 (ESV) — "For God so loved the world, that he gave his only Son, that whoever believes in him should not perish but have eternal life."

As Judge He is fair—
Knows exactly what's right.
I can trust what He says
For He loves me in spite . . .

Of the times I am naughty,
The times I am nice.
My debt has been paid—
I've been bought with a price.

That's why He's Redeemer,
He covered my sin—
Washed the stains out,
I'm clean from within.

1 Peter 1:18-19 (NIV) — "For you know that it was not with perishable things such as silver or gold that you were redeemed from the empty way of life handed down to you from your ancestors, but with the precious blood of Christ, a lamb without blemish or defect."

O Jesus, You're King
So worthy of praise—
I give you my heart,
My hands I will raise.

For no other God
Is so mighty and true.
No other God
Is as holy as You.

Isaiah 45:21 (ESV) — " . . . And there is no other god besides me, a righteous God and a Savior; there is none besides me."

You created the heavens,
Spoke the world into order.
Told the seas where to stop—
You established their borders.

Psalm 33:6-7 (ESV) — "By the word of the LORD the heavens were made, and by the breath of his mouth all their host. He gathers the waters of the sea as a heap; he puts the deeps in storehouses."

Genesis 1:1 (ESV) — "In the beginning, God created the heavens and the earth."
Genesis 1:25 (ESV) — "And God made the beasts of the earth according to their kinds . . . and everything that creeps on the ground according to its kind . . . "

You made all the creatures,
Scales, feathers, and hair—
From wiggly worm
To the great grizzly bear.

Genesis 1:27 (ESV) — "So God created man in his own image, in the image of God he created him; male and female, he created them."

**But Your greatest creation,
The one that stands out—
Reflects Your image.
It's me! So I'll shout . . .**

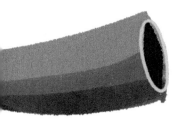

How You give me a purpose,
And love beyond measure,
You call me Your own—
To You I am treasured!

1 Peter 2:9 (ESV) — "But you are a chosen race, a royal priesthood, a holy nation, a people for his own possession, that you may proclaim the excellencies of him who called you out of darkness into his marvelous light."

Lord, You're also Provider,
Many blessings abound—
To count them all up
Makes my head spin around.

Philippians 4:19 (NIV) — "And my God will meet all your needs according to the riches of his glory in Christ Jesus."

So now I know why
You are my strong tower—
You're loving, and holy,
And mighty in power.

Psalm 147:5 (NIV) — "Great is our Lord, and mighty in power; his understanding has no limit."

For You are my Comforter,
You are my Guide,
To You I will run—
I'll find shelter inside.

Psalm 91:1 (ESV) — "He who dwells in the shelter of the Most High will abide in the shadow of the Almighty."

About the Author

Hello! I'm LeAnne. I'm probably not too different from you—balancing a variety of roles and feeling like I'm floundering with most. But I've got a big God who loves taking the weak and ordinary and infusing them with His might. Through God's power, I'm an author and speaker and have been a Bible teacher for nearly three decades.

My husband Ron and I have two grown kids—both are married now! Each addition enlarged our family and deepened our joy. We love to travel, serve the Church, and help missionaries around the globe. We live in the beautiful mountains of east Tennessee.

For more information about
God's Name is a Tower
please visit:

www.leanneblackmore.com
www.facebook.com/authorleanneblackmore
bmore@comcast.net
@blackmoreauthor

For more information about
AMBASSADOR INTERNATIONAL
please visit:
www.ambassador-international.com
@AmbassadorIntl
www.facebook.com/AmbassadorIntl